May enjoy ma.... ....
with Faith as you read to
her and watch her grow.

Love,

Jyst Family

7

Marty Johnson

June 7, 2006

Raise Up A Child

BY MARTY JOHNSON

PHOTOGRAPHY BY SUE ANTONSEN

AN EMJ ENTERPRISES PUBLICATION

Copyright information for biblical texts:
Scripture taken from THE MESSAGE. Copyright by Eugene H. Peterson, 1993, 1994,
1995. Used by permission of NavPress Publishing Group.
Scripture taken from the King James Version (KJV). Copyright © 1970 by Thomas
Nelson Inc. Camden, New Jersey 08103.
Scripture taken from the New Revised Standard Version (NRSV). Copyright © 1989
by Thomas Nelson Publishers, Nashville, with permission of the National Council of
Churches of Christ in the United States of America.
The "Lord's Prayer" (page 74) and the "Ten Commandments" (page 75) are
quoted from Deharbe's Large Catechism, Benziger Brothers, New York, 1882.

Text copyright © 2001 Marty Johnson
Photographs copyright © 2001 Sue Antonsen

Edited by Matthew Johnson

Cover and book design by Hanna Design Limited

Printed in the United States of America

An EMJ Enterprises publication
P.O. Box 260290
Highlands Ranch, CO 80163-0290
For inquiries call toll-free 1-877-801-5928
Visit: www.emjenterprises.com or www.raiseupachild.com
ISBN 0-9679590-1-2

Library of Congress Control Number: 2001091752

First Edition; Second Printing

Raise Up A Child

TRAIN CHILDREN IN THE RIGHT WAY,

AND WHEN OLD,

THEY WILL NOT STRAY.

Proverbs 22:6 (NRSV)

So here's what I want you to do, God helping you: Take your everyday, ordinary life—your sleeping, eating, going-to-work, and walking-around life—and place it before God as an offering. Embracing what God does for you is the best thing you can do for him. Don't become so well-adjusted to your culture that you fit into it without even thinking. Instead, fix your attention on God. You'll be changed from the inside out. Readily recognize what he wants from you, and quickly respond to it. Unlike the culture around you, always dragging you down to its level of immaturity, God brings the best out of you, develops well-formed maturity in you.

Romans 12:1-2 (The Message)

In memory of my parents

ERLEEN AND PFC FREDERIC BERNIER (WWII VETERAN)

1943

*T*he most formative moments in our lives are often found among our most common everyday experiences and choices. It is in these ordinary events that we can encounter and teach to our children the joy and importance of abiding in the presence of God daily. The translation of Romans 12:1-2 in *The Message* (a contemporary rendering of the New Testament) expresses this idea beautifully:

> So here's what I want you to do, God helping you: Take your everyday, ordinary life—your sleeping, eating, going-to-work, and walking-around life—and place it before God as an offering. Embracing what God does for you is the best thing you can do for him. Don't become so well-adjusted to your culture that you fit into it without even thinking. Instead, fix your attention on God. You'll be changed from the inside out. Readily recognize what he wants from you, and quickly respond to it. Unlike the culture around you, always dragging you down to its level of immaturity, God brings the best out of you, develops well-formed maturity in you.

It is from this perspective that I have written this collection of poems that speaks to our "everyday, ordinary lives"—some to inspire, with thoughts about God and life, and some to simply "tickle" the heart with fun, light-hearted themes. The poems dealing with God and spiritual issues are deliberately interspersed among those about the more ordinary things of life (e.g. kittens, caramel candy, Mommies and Daddies, etc.). This is done to emphasize that these two aspects of life are tightly intertwined and that the wonder and mystery of God are to be found in the most common of vessels. I have used Summer, Fall, Winter and Spring to begin each chapter, for two reasons: To frame the richness of life's simple pleasures within each season, and for the changing of the same, to remind us that, "To everything there is a season" (Ecclesiastes 3:1 [KJV]; see, "Pumpkins and Spices" page 39).

I have observed, among my own grandchildren, that rhyming about everyday events creates an atmosphere of joy, where smiles are abundant and hearts are light. My mother often said, "An ounce of prevention is worth a pound of cure." And so, I rhyme a lot when I'm with my grandkids, keeping the mood lifted and happy. There is a simple, yet touching, little rhyme called "Doodly Doo" (see page 24) that is one of their favorites. Once, while reading my poems in my granddaughter's class and using her name in "Doodly Doo," an adorable little boy raised his hand and asked: "Could you say my name in that?" I replied, "Of course, I can," and asked, "How many others would like their name said in this rhyme?" Every hand went flying up! Each child listened with a deep smile as their name was included.

Rhyming is also a quick and fun way to teach children to memorize. It's like gymnastics for the brain. I noticed it was after rhyming that my children and grandchildren were better able to memorize other sayings and prayers. At the end of this book I have included the 23rd Psalm, the Lord's Prayer and the Ten Commandments, just as I memorized them as a child. I feel it is important to have children start memorizing traditional prayers at a young age. Even if they do not understand them initially, their way of thinking and behaving will begin to be formed by them. I try never to underestimate the spiritual depth of a child or their ability to learn. When I was very young, and in Sunday school, I preferred learning prayers to cut-and-paste or coloring. Even when I was in kindergarten, I loved to hear the Ten Commandments read and discussed. When I attended public school, in Maine, we did discuss the Ten Commandments and even recited scripture in the classroom. Nowadays, children do not have that opportunity at school, so it is even more important to give them every possible chance to hear and to memorize these at home. Our children should leave our homes "trained-up" and "filled-up" with the goodness of God. For the Bible says: "Train children in the right way, and when old, they will not stray" (Proverbs 22:6, NRSV).

Recognizing the importance of a loving family, I would like to acknowledge each member of my family, whose talents and hard work have made this book possible.

To my daughter, Sue Antonsen: Thank you for all the wonderful photographs that you have taken over the last eight years. Because of your efforts, we were able to find the perfect pictures for the poetry and rhymes in *Raise Up A Child.* Sue, you lift the spirit with your photography, and in a split-second turn normal events in one's life into celebrations and works of art! (It should be noted that Sue and I worked independently and only collaborated over this last year.)

To my husband, Ed, and our two sons, Ed, Jr. (Eddie) and Matthew: Your talents helped to make this book a reality; Eddie, for your publishing and promotional skills; Matthew, for your editing and scripture research; and Ed, for your laying the operational foundation and organizing the practical effort. Thanks, guys!

To my daughters-in-law, Mary Johnson and Franziska Johnson, and my son-in-law, Don Antonsen: Your willingness to help out in any and every way is greatly appreciated!

A dear friend of mine made an adorable bookmarker for me, using her favorite quote from Charles Dickens: "It is not a slight thing when they, who are so fresh from God, love us." It is with this sentiment that I thank each one of my grandchildren. You are a continual source of joy and inspiration in all of our lives.

In addition to my family, I want to offer a special thanks to Cheryl Patrick of Hanna Design whose graphics work on this book and my previous book, *Christmas Time In My House,* exceeded my expectations. Cheryl, working with you is a pleasure.

It was thirty-seven years ago that Ed and I were married by our parish priest, before our friends and family. The marriage certificate we signed stated what our home should be: "A little church within a church." Continuing on, it admonished: "Your home shall be a haven where two tables are spread—one for the food of the body, and one for the nourishment of the soul."

It is our hope that *Raise Up A Child* will help inspire families to that end—not only in our lifetime, but in the lifetimes of those who will come after us.

- **Marty Johnson**

Summer

Do You See What I See?

Do you see what i see?
Come and listen carefully.
I will show you when you ask.
There we'll sit, in the sun we'll bask.

See the fish that jumps out there?
Yes, that one without a care.
Well, he knows the one above,
The one who's made us in his LOVE.
Don't you worry—can't you see?—
That fish he made for you and me.

Inspired by: Genesis 1:20-23, 28

*The One who's
made us in
His love*

Rocky Mountain National Park, CO

*That fish he made for
you and me.*

The Path Is Clear

THE LIGHT THAT LIGHTS MY PATH IS CLEAR;
IT'S CLEAR BOTH NIGHT AND DAY;
IT'S SIMPLE, VERY SIMPLE;
LISTEN, AND HEAR HIM SAY:
"WON'T YOU ENTER IN AND STAY?"

Inspired by: Psalm 119:105, Hebrews 4:7

Come And Sing A Silly Song

Come and sing a silly song,
Come with me and sing along.
Rhyme a line or two with me,
Then you'll see, we'll both agree.
When you do, you won't regret.
Never, never, EVER fret!

Burping Babies, Buggies And So

Burping babies, buggies and so;
Off to playing we will go
To the park to fly a kite,
Up so high, with all our might!

Burping babies, buggies and so;
Off to playing we will go
To the beach, toes in the sand,
Castle building with our hands!

Burping babies, buggies and so;
Off to playing we will go
To the mountains, up so high,
Snow covered tops that reach the sky.

Burping babies, buggies and so;
Off to playing we will go
In the backyard, on the swing,
Hanging, climbing, ring-a-ding-ding!

Burping babies, buggies and so;
Off to playing we will go!

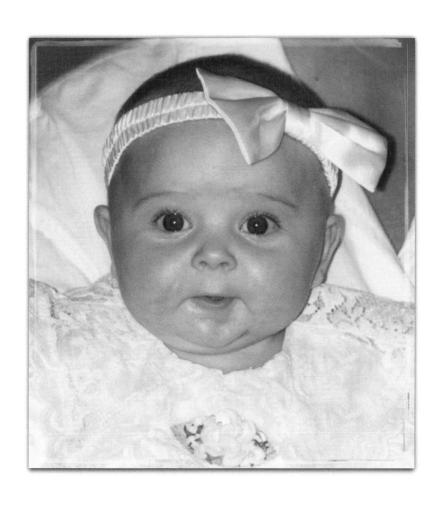

Off to playing we will go!

Popsicles

Popsicles, popsicles are a big treat.
If I could choose, that's all I would eat.
I think that I know what's good for me;
If only my mommy and daddy agreed!

Caramel Candy

Caramel candy, trips to the zoo,
Sunny warm days, walking with you;
These are the things that I will remember,
Not only from January on through December,
But all of my days until I get grown,
And do these same things with kids of my own!

These are the things that I will remember all of my days until I get grown,

Sunshiny Weather

Sunshiny weather,
Birds of a feather,
Playing from dawn until dusk, you and me;
Sunshiny weather,
Playing together
Is where i want to be.

Sunshiny weather,
Blue skies so high,
Clouds' whispering shadows catching my eye;
Come play and see,
Friends we shall be;
Don't miss the sunshiny weather with me.

Playing from
dawn until dusk,

you and me

Honolulu, Hawaii

Doodly Doo

ABIGAIL, ABIGAIL, DOODLY DOO;
I LOVE, I LOVE, I LOVE YOU!
ABIGAIL, ABIGAIL, DOODLY DEE;
YOU LOVE, YOU LOVE, YOU LOVE ME!

BENJAMIN, BENJAMIN, DOODLY DOO. . .

CAMILLE, CAMILLE, DOODLY DOO. . .

DANIEL, DANIEL, DOODLY DOO. . .

(I repeat this rhyme over and over with each of my grandchildren. As you can see by the above examples, you can substitute any child's name into this fun, everyday rhyme. I've done it with classrooms of students one at a time or in a group—e.g. "Polar Bears, Polar Bears, doodly doo. . .")

Bubbles In My Tubbles

I PUT BUBBLES IN MY TUBBLES

AND IT MAKES ME WANNA SCRUBBLES;

IT MAKES ME WANNA SCRUBBLES EVERY DAY.

I PUT BUBBLES IN MY TUBBLES

AND IT MAKES ME WANNA SCRUBBLES;

IT MAKES ME WANNA SCRUBBLES,

HIPPITY-HIP-HOORAY!

(A fun rhyme to sing to a child at bath time!)

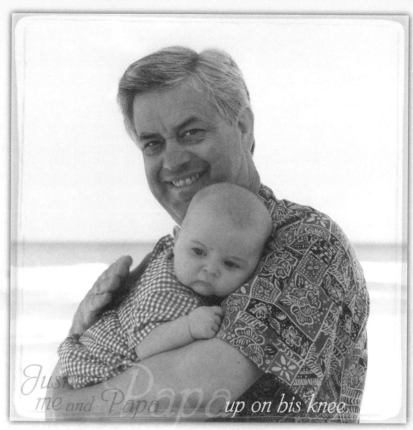

Just me and Papa up on his knee.

Netanya, Israel

Papa's Knee

Climbing & rhyming—these are fun.
I like to do them;
I like to run!
But, some of the time,
I like to be still;
Not running or rhyming,
Or climbing up hills.
I just like to sit,
I just like to be.
Just me and Papa—up on his knee.

A Mystery

Jesus lives within my heart
And we'll never, ever part.
The HOLY SPIRIT gave me to say:
"Come into my heart today!"
Yes, i know,
You are the way—
The way that leads to the Father,
Where forever i will stay!

Inspired by: John 14:6, Colossians 2:2-3

Raise Up A Child

Raise Up A Child

Fall

Hide-And-Go-Seek

SOMETHING'S COMING DOWN THE ROAD.
WHATEVER IT IS, I DO NOT KNOW.
IS IT A RABBIT, HOG OR TOAD?

SOMETHING'S COMING DOWN THE ROAD.
WHERE'S IT GOING? WHAT'LL IT BE?
I'LL JUST HAVE TO WAIT AND SEE.

UNLESS, I GO EXPLORE A BIT;
WILL IT COME TO ME, OR WILL I GO TO IT?
WHAT DO YOU SUPPOSE I'LL DO?
WILL I JUST BE SURPRISED?—BY WHO?

NO, I DON'T THINK I'LL WAIT AND LOOK;
DON'T THINK I'LL GO READ A BOOK.
HOLD ON, JUST WAIT, I THINK I SEE,
FROM MY HIDING PLACE UP IN THIS TREE;
IT'S ONLY DADDY FINDING ME!

From my biding

place up in this tree;

It's only Daddy finding me.

Red Leaves

Bright red leaves fall to the ground;
Just a whispery silent sound;
Purple, orange and yellow, too;
A carpet of leaves for me and you.

Oh, Jesus

Oh, Jesus,
You light the path that i walk on,
And you are the one that i love.
Yes, you are coming for me
From your heavenly throne up above.
But today is the day that i need you.
Yes, today i need you near.
Speak to this one who is seeking;
Where you are, there is no fear.

Inspired by: Psalm 119:105, 2 Timothy 1:7, Matthew 7:7-8

Daddy And Me

On daddy's back i like to sit;
We roll and laugh and play a bit.
He lifts me high up in the air;
I am a bird without a care!
Daddy and i have so much fun.
I hit the ball and then i run.
I hide from him; he hides from me,
And then i find him, yessiree!
But sometimes we just like to sit,
To listen and to think a bit.
Now that i've shared my poem with you,
Let's see if you can do one, too!

Fall Nights

Clouds up high in the dark of night,
Paint the sky while the moon shines bright.
It peaks through clear skies, here and there,
Inviting everyone to stare.
The yellow trees upon the ground—
A bright bouquet—do not make a sound.
Yes, that's right,
I love fall nights!

A Secret Place

THERE IS A SECRET PLACE TO DWELL,
A SPECIAL PLACE, SO LISTEN WELL.
IT WAS PREPARED FOR YOU AND ME,
FOR NOW AND FOR ETERNITY!

HE CAME FROM HEAVEN, ON DOWN TO EARTH,
TO TRADE HIS LIFE FOR OUR "NEW BIRTH."
NO ONE TOOK HIS LIFE, YOU SEE,
HE LAID IT DOWN FOR YOU AND ME.

THERE IS A SECRET PLACE TO DWELL,
JUST ASK "THE WOMAN AT THE WELL."
SHE TOOK HIS WORDS FOR ALL TO HEAR,
AND KNEW SHE'D SEEN HER SAVIOR, DEAR.
"WHERE IS THIS HIDING PLACE?" YOU SAY,
AND "MAY I ENTER IN TODAY?"
THE ANSWER'S NEAR.
FOR HE'S THE WAY!

Inspired by: Psalm 91, John 4:5-42 (Woman at the well)

Sleepy Kitten

SLEEPY KITTEN,
PAWS LIKE MITTENS,
THINK I'LL SING YOU A LULLABY.
CLOSE YOUR EYES NOW,
DREAM SWEET DREAMS,
WE'LL PLAY AGAIN, BY-AND-BY.

Just Beyond The Hill

My friend and I went walking by
A pumpkin patch one day.
We said, "oh yes, this is a place
Where we would like to play."
. . . The pumpkins round upon the ground,
Big orange pumpkins that we found. . .
We stayed and played,
And played and stayed,
Until we had our fill
Of playing in the pumpkin patch
Just beyond the hill.

My friend and I went walking by

pumpkins round upon the ground

Snohomish, Washington

Any Day

Any day,
I would say,
Is a perfect time to do
All the things you know are right,
What GOD asks of you.

What does he ask of me?
How am i to know?
His laws are written in our hearts,
And the bible tells us so.

But what the Lord asks of me,
Above all else, is plain to see,
Is faith in him through Jesus.
Yes, he loves me, and from above,
He delights in giving to me and receiving all my LOVE!

Inspired by: Psalm 119:30, Jeremiah 31:33, John 6:29, Hebrews, 11:6

Back 'round once again.

Pumpkins And Spices

Pumpkins and spices,

All part of fall,

Cold, crispy days,

Made for us all;

To remind us that everything

Comes to an end,

And everything comes

Back 'round once again.

Inspired by: Ecclesiastes 3:1

Winter

Celebrate

Christmas is a time to sing;
A time for joy;
Let all bells ring
The news of Christ,
The newborn King!

The Bread Of Life

God's gift to us came from above,
From there he sent his perfect love.
This gift would set the captives free—
Set captives free for all to see.

His yoke is easy, his burden is light,
This gift was born one starry night.
The BREAD OF LIFE was born, you see,
In BETHLEHEM for you and me.

Inspired by: John 6:35, Matthew 11:28
(A note of interest: The Hebrew name
"Bethlehem" means "House of Bread")

Unto us a
child is born...

Born In A Manger

He was born in a manger;
A stranger to earth.
He came down from heaven
For our "new birth."
From a hill he would rise
To heaven above,
Where he waits to receive us
In his perfect love.

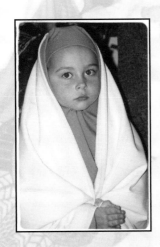

Snowflakes were falling

As fast as could be.

Snowflakes

I woke up this morning
And said, "look and see!"
Snowflakes were falling
As fast as could be.
Snowflakes were falling
All over the trees,
All over the ground,
All over the sidewalks,
All over the town!
I just couldn't wait,
I just had to play
In the snow that was made
From the snowflakes today!

Icicle Elephants

When I was a child I loved to play
Out in the snow all of the day.
I'd carve an igloo, an elephant, too,
And other animals from the zoo.
Now when the carving was all through,
There was one thing I had to do
To keep them standing days-on-end,
To have them, play and just pretend:
My dad and I would sprinkle them "good,"
So they could stand up like they should.
Icicle elephants, igloos, too,
My wintry friends, I'll share with you.

Melting Snow

When snow upon the ground, so white,
Is lighting up the dark of night,
I love to walk, see trees that bow
Under the weight of heavy snow.
But when the snow begins to melt
It brings a certain sadness felt;
When summer's far away, not near,
A meadowlark we cannot hear.

So white the snow, so cold my nose;
My spirit sings in sweet repose:
"I do not like the melting snow."

Perfection

THIS LIFE WON'T EVER BE PERFECT.

NO, LIFE ISN'T ALWAYS FAIR!

BUT YOU CAN MAKE QUITE A DIFFERENCE,

IF ABIDING IN HIM, YOU WILL SHARE:

THE LOVE HE'S FREELY GIVEN;

THE LOVE HE HAS GIVEN TO YOU.

THIS LOVE FROM ABOVE IS PERFECT,

NO MATTER HOW DARK, IT WILL ALWAYS SHINE THROUGH!

Inspired by: 1 John 4:18-21, Matthew 22:37-39

Love from above is Perfect

No matter how dark,
it will always shine through!

49

Daydreaming
Sunny Days
Butterflies

Winter in Honolulu, Hawaii

Daydreaming Sunny Days

Daydreaming, sunny days, birds in the sky,
Butterflies—whispering—wings flutter by.

Sing me this song, now we are here;
Daydreaming, sunny days, so very near.

Daydreaming, sunny days, birds in the sky,
Butterflies—whispering—wings flutter by.

Just close your eyes, dream of bright sunny skies,
And in a twinkling the winter's gone by!

Kittens

Kittens, mittens,
Warm cozy things;
These rhyme when i say them,
Like "ring-a-ding-ding!"
And did you know
Just one other thing?
When i hold a kitten
It makes my heart sing!

Warm cozy things

It makes my *heart* *sing!*

Every Knee Shall Bow

There is a mystery, i am told,
A story, true and very old.
From the bible it is clear,
There's one who loves us and he's near.

Not all will know him, not all will see;
Not all will choose to believe.
His love is great, he gave us choice,
He doesn't force us to rejoice
In the one who came from above;
We can refuse him and his love.

But, one day, every eye shall see,
And everyone will bow their knee
To the one who died on calvary.
He's coming again for you and me!

Inspired by: Joshua 24:15, Deuteronomy 11:26-28,
Philippians 2:9-11, Acts 1:9-11

Jesus

Jesus, Jesus, Jesus,
How I love your name.
My heart bows down in your presence.
For your love to me remains
Safe in the hands of the Father,
The Son and the Holy Ghost.
My love for you is safe,
Because you love me the most.

Inspired by: 1 John 4:19, Romans 8:37-39

Spring

It's your love that he seeks.

Do You Hear?

Do you hear?
Do you know?
Do you want to?
Does it show?

Do you hear him when he speaks?
It's your love that he seeks.
Do you really want to know?
If you do, and if you will,
Answer his call from calvary's hill,
Then you will be forever filled!

Inspired by: Isaiah 28:23, Hebrews 4:7

Venice, Italy

His Life

He died that we could live;
He gave that we could give;
He will come again;
His love will never end.

Where Is He?

He's not still in a tomb,
Though born in a stable;
He died on the cross,
Because he was able
To raise himself up on the third day, you see.
He raised himself up for you and for me.

His throne is in heaven, in heaven above,
And from that high place we receive the great love
From a Father who loves us so much that he gave
The gift we needed, that we might be saved!

Inspired by: 1 Corinthians 15:3-4, Revelation 5:13,
Mark 16:19, Colossians 3:1

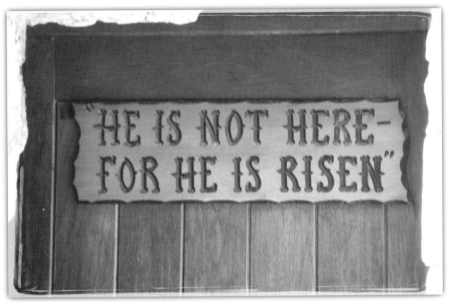

Jerusalem, Israel

Every Day

DUM-DEEDLE-DUM-DEEDLE-DUM-DEEDLE-DEE,
EVERY DAY HE WALKS WITH ME.
HE WALKS WITH ME, AND IF YOU CHOOSE,
EVERY DAY HE'LL WALK WITH YOU.

Inspired by: Psalm 56:13

Tulip Time

YELLOW TULIPS, TIPS OF PURPLE,
POP THEIR HEADS UP IN A CIRCLE.
PLANTED BY MY NANA SO
I CAN PICK THEM WHEN THEY GROW;
PLANTED JUST FOR ME TO SEE,
RIGHT BELOW THE BIG PLUM TREE.
SOME RED AND WHITE, PINK AND PURPLE,
POP THEIR HEADS UP IN A CIRCLE.
BULBS BELOW THE GROUND SO COLD;
WARMED UP NOW, SO THEY CAN GROW.

Rainy Days

"It rained all night," my mommy said,
But i was cozy in my bed.
This morning, rain's still coming down,
But drops on me will not be found.
For i will play right in my room,
With cars and things that go crash and boom!
No, rain all day won't spoil my play.
I'll just have fun inside, today.

Worms

Do you like worms?
Well, i do,
Not in my lunch box,
Not in my stew.
I like to hold them and feel them wiggle.
They make me happy;
They make me giggle.

Don't want to feel them squish between my toes!
Don't want a worm hanging from my nose!
I just like to hold them for a little while,
And then put them back in a big dirt pile.

Mommies

Some mommies are pretty; some mommies will play;
Some mommies are busy all of the day.
My mommy is all of these things, you see,
But never too busy to say to me:
"Come join me for a cup of tea!"

Uncles and Aunties

Dear uncles we have,
Dear aunties have we,
And when we want fun,
It's where they will be!

My mommy is all of these things, you see

Come join me for a cup of tea!

One-Of-A-Kind

Just never you mind,
I'm one-of-a-kind!
I'm precious and dear,
God's creation, you hear!
Just never you mind,
I'm one-of-a-kind.

Inspired by: Psalm 139:13-14

I'm precious and dear,

God's creation,

you hear!

My Jesus

When I'm in bed at night and the lights are out,
I think a lot and wonder, too,
what everything's about;
I close my eyes real tight,
And think with all my might;
Who is this I hear?
Who says: "I'm very near!"
Oh yes, now I know,
It's MY JESUS—HE LOVES ME SO!

Inspired by: Revelation 3:20

Sleeping

It's time for me to go to sleep,
But I don't think I'll count those sheep.
I won't count cows, they only moo.
I won't count sniggly diggly twos.
I won't count pets, my nose or bows.
I won't count wriggly tiggly toes.
I bet I have you really guessing;
But now, I'll tell: I'll count my blessings.

My Jesus
He Loves Me So

It's time for me to go to sleep

I'll count
my blessings

Traditional Prayers

The Grounds of St. Thomas More Catholic Church,
Englewood, CO

The 23rd Psalm

THE LORD IS MY SHEPHERD; I SHALL NOT WANT.
HE MAKETH ME TO LIE DOWN IN GREEN PASTURES:
HE LEADETH ME BESIDE THE STILL WATERS.
HE RESTORETH MY SOUL: HE LEADETH ME IN THE PATHS OF
RIGHTEOUSNESS FOR HIS NAME'S SAKE.
YEA, THOUGH I WALK THROUGH THE VALLEY OF THE SHADOW
OF DEATH, I WILL FEAR NO EVIL: FOR THOU ART WITH ME;
THY ROD AND THY STAFF THEY COMFORT ME.
THOU PREPAREST A TABLE BEFORE ME IN THE PRESENCE OF
MINE ENEMIES: THOU ANOINTEST MY HEAD WITH OIL;
MY CUP RUNNETH OVER.
SURELY GOODNESS AND MERCY SHALL FOLLOW ME ALL THE DAYS
OF MY LIFE: AND I WILL DWELL IN THE HOUSE OF THE LORD
FOR EVER. (KJV)

The Lord
    is my shepherd

Cascade Mountains, Washington State

The Lord's Prayer

OUR FATHER WHO ART IN HEAVEN,

HALLOWED BE THY NAME;

THY KINGDOM COME;

THY WILL BE DONE ON EARTH AS IT IS IN HEAVEN;

GIVE US THIS DAY OUR DAILY BREAD;

AND FORGIVE US OUR TRESPASSES AS WE FORGIVE THEM

WHO TRESPASS AGAINST US;

AND LEAD US NOT INTO TEMPTATION;

BUT DELIVER US FROM EVIL. AMEN.

Deharbe's Large Catechism, 1882 (Matthew 6:9–13)

The Ten Commandments

I AM THE LORD THY GOD, WHO BROUGHT THEE OUT OF
THE LAND OF EGYPT, AND OUT OF THE HOUSE OF BONDAGE.

I. THOU SHALT NOT HAVE STRANGE GODS BEFORE ME;
THOU SHALT NOT MAKE TO THYSELF ANY GRAVEN THING,
NOR THE LIKENESS OF ANYTHING THAT IS IN THE HEAVENS ABOVE,
OR IN THE EARTH BENEATH, OR IN THE WATERS UNDER THE EARTH.
THOU SHALT NOT ADORE THEM NOR SERVE THEM.

II. THOU SHALT NOT TAKE THE NAME OF THE LORD THY GOD IN VAIN.

III. REMEMBER THAT THOU KEEP HOLY THE SABBATH-DAY.

IV. HONOR THY FATHER AND THY MOTHER THAT IT MAY BE
WELL WITH THEE,
AND THOU MAYEST LIVE LONG ON THE EARTH.

V. THOU SHALT NOT KILL.

VI. THOU SHALT NOT COMMIT ADULTERY.

VII. THOU SHALT NOT STEAL.

VIII. THOU SHALT NOT BEAR FALSE WITNESS AGAINST THY NEIGHBOR.

IX. THOU SHALT NOT COVET THY NEIGHBOR'S WIFE.

X. THOU SHALT NOT COVET THY NEIGHBOR'S GOODS.

Deharbe's Large Catechism, 1882 (Deuteronomy 5:6-21)

"If one advances confidently in the direction of his dreams, and endeavors to live the life which he has imagined, he will meet with a success unexpected in common hours."

— HENRY DAVID THOREAU

The Johnson Family, Thanksgiving Day 1999,
Highlands Ranch, Colorado

Marty Johnson - Author

Marty Johnson, the author of two books—*Raise Up A Child* and *Christmas Time In My House*—shares a "kindred spirit" (love of God, family life and traveling) with her husband, Ed. After one of many trips to Jerusalem, Israel, she was inspired to write this particular collection of poems and rhymes. As a Christian, Marty celebrates the Lord's love for us through the eyes of a child in her poetry, intended for young and old, alike.

Marty enjoying a stroll with her grandson on the "world-famous" Ben Yehuda St., Jerusalem, Israel. The whole family was there for Matthew and Franziska's wedding in April of 1996.

Sue Antonsen - Photographer

Sue Antonsen received her BA degree in Elementary Education from Western Washington University, where she had the opportunity to study abroad. Sue's interest in photography began to take shape on a trip to Siena, Italy (1990-91). Her photography has been inspired by the beautiful places where she has lived and visited, but above all she enjoys photographing the everyday activities of children. Her nephew and niece and her own children are her greatest inspirations and give her many opportunities to capture the gentle, joyful qualities that are unique to children. The photographs in this book have been taken in Italy, Israel, Washington State, Hawaii and Colorado. Sue and her husband, Don, first met in junior high school in Kirkland, WA, and now live in Highlands Ranch, CO with their two children.

Sue holding some of her "inspirations"— nephew (left) niece (right) son (middle) 1999.

Ed Johnson, Jr. – Publisher

Ed Johnson, Jr., owner of EMJ Enterprises (founded in February 2000), is the publisher of *Raise Up A Child* and *Christmas Time In My House*. In addition to publishing, his company also imports scripture-based ceramic tiles (collectible wall hangings) from Jerusalem, Israel. A retired police officer, Ed is fulfilling a lifelong dream of owning his own "family business." He and his wife, Mary, have been married for 12 years and live in Colorado with their two children. Ed enjoys travel and hiking in the beautiful Rocky Mountains with his family.

Ed, Jr. seen here after reaching the top while hiking in the mountains of British Columbia in 1992.

Matthew in one of the many garden areas of the Tayellet, a beautiful park in Jerusalem, Israel, just before his wedding in 1996.

Matthew Johnson – Editor

Raise Up A Child is Matthew's second professional editing project. His first book, *Christians and Israel*, was published in 1996. He recently received his MA degree in Theology and Jewish Studies from the University of St. Michael's College (Toronto), where he wrote his thesis on the State of Israel in Catholic-Jewish relations. He and his wife, Franziska, met and married in Jerusalem, Israel, and are currently living in Highlands Ranch, CO.

Ed Johnson, Sr. – Production

After 33 years in the corporate world, Ed, Sr. decided it was time to refresh himself and the family. In 1999, he retired from his corporate position and took a 3-month trip to Israel with his wife, Marty, to visit their son Matthew who was completing his masters degree in Jerusalem. After returning from Israel, and moving from the state of Washington to Colorado, he threw himself into supporting his oldest son's (Ed, Jr.) desire to start a publishing business. The result is *Christmas Time In My House* and *Raise Up A Child*, published by EMJ Enterprises.

Ed, Sr. enjoying a bench stop while in Caesarea, Israel, during the family's 1996 visit.

Other Books By Marty Johnson

Christmas Time In My House

Text copyright © 1980 by Marty Johnson
Illustrations copyright © 1997 by Franziska Johnson

A classic Christmas poem that rekindles all of your favorite memories
of this joyful season. This 24-page, high quality hardback book, with
10 full-page heartwarming illustrations, is beautiful enough to display
in your home. It is sure to become a part of your family's Christmas
tradition for generations to come!

An EMJ Enterprises publication
P.O. Box 260290
Highlands Ranch, CO 80163-0290

For inquiries call toll-free 1-877-801-5928
Visit: **www.emjenterprises.com** or **www.christmastimeinmyhouse.com**